SNOOPY STARS
—AS—
LUDWIG
VAN BEAGLE

Charles M. Schulz

ℛ
RAVETTE BOOKS

First published by
Ravette Books Limited 1990

Printed and bound in Great Britain
for Ravette Books Limited,
3 Glenside Estate, Star Road, Partridge Green,
Horsham, West Sussex RH13 8RA
by Cox & Wyman Ltd, Reading

ISBN 1 85304 234 X

12-15

IF THE COUNTESS HADN'T TURNED HIM DOWN, WOULD YOU BUY ME SOMETHING?

I HAVE A QUESTION I'D LIKE TO ASK YOU..

WHAT MAKES YOU THINK BEETHOVEN WAS BETTER THAN ELTON JOHN?

4-6

10-26

5-14

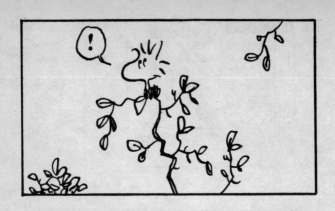

7-31

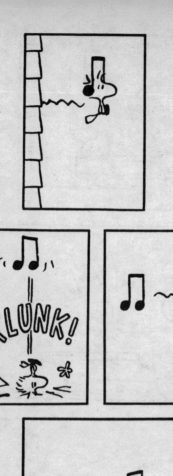

© 1977 United Feature Syndicate, Inc.

4-26

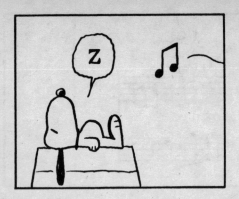

DO YOU THINK IT'S POSSIBLE THAT I'M YOUR FAVORITE PERSON IN THE WHOLE WIDE WORLD?

HAHAHAHA

SUDDENLY I'M A STAND-UP COMIC

8-20

© 1980 United Feature Syndicate, Inc.

SCHULZ

4-15

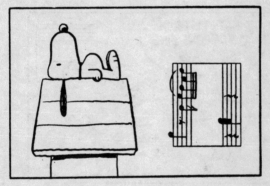

12-27

4-17

BOING!!

5-3

SURPRISE!

© 1984 United Feature Syndicate, Inc.

WHAT'S THIS?

IT'S A CUPCAKE! HAPPY BEETHOVEN'S BIRTHDAY!

© 1983 United Feature Syndicate, Inc.

9-18

I BROUGHT SOME OF MY VACATION PICTURES FOR YOU TO SEE, SCHROEDER, BUT I GUESS YOU'RE BUSY...

WHY DON'T I JUST LEAVE THEM HERE, AND YOU CAN LOOK AT THEM LATER?

YOU WERE RIGHT...THE LID WAS OFF THE JAR

NO ONE CAN SLEEP WITH A BUNCH OF CHOCOLATE CHIP COOKIES SINGING ALL NIGHT..

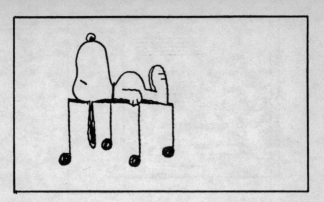

9-14

1-3-88   © 1987 United Feature Syndicate, Inc.

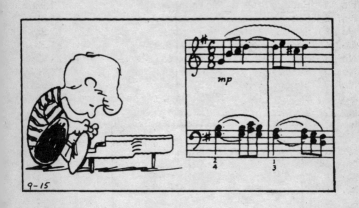

© 1988 United Feature Syndicate, Inc. SCHULZ

Other Snoopy titles published by Ravette Books

Black and white landscapes

It's a Dog's Life	£2.50
Roundup	£2.50
Freewheelin'	£2.50
Joe Cool	£2.50
Chariots For Hire	£2.50
Dogs Don't Eat Dessert	£2.50
You're on the Wrong Foot Again, Charlie Brown	£2.50
By Supper Possessed	£2.95
Talk is Cheep, Charlie Brown	£2.95

Weekenders

No. 1 Weekender	£4.95

Brothers & Sisters It's All Relative	£3.95
Peanuts at School	£6.95

All these books are available at your local bookshop or news-agent, or can be ordered direct from the publisher. Just tick the titles you require and fill in the form below. Prices and availability subject to change without notice.

Ravette Books Limited, 3 Glenside Estate, Star Road, Partridge Green, Horsham, West Sussex RH13 8RA

Please send a cheque or postal order, and allow the following for postage and packing. UK: Snoopy Stars – 45p for one book, 20p for a second book and 15p for each additional book. Other titles – 50p for one book and 30p for each additional book.

Name ....

Address ....

....